# Th

# Brontë Sisters

# Quiz

**DATE DUE** )k

| | | | |
|---|---|---|---|
| | | | |
| | | | |
| | | | |
| | | | |
| | | | |
| | | | |
| | | | |
| | | | |
| | | | |
| | | | |
| | | | |
| | | | |
| | | | |
| | | | |
| | | | |
| | | | |
| | | | |
| | | | |

arton

First published 1998
Reprinted 2002
© Helen Barton 1998

ISBN 0-9527257-9-7

Published by Helen Barton.
Printed by Aspect Design.

*For Alex, Sam, Thomas and Eleanor.*

*In memory of my father.*

# Contents

# THE BRONTË SISTERS AND THEIR FAMILY

1. Name the three Brontë sisters.

2. Who wrote "Jane Eyre" and who wrote "Wuthering Heights"?

3. Where did the Brontë family live?

4. Anne Brontë wrote two novels. Can you name them both?

5. Are the following statements true or false?

   a) Patrick Brontë was a clergyman.
   b) Maria Brontë came from Yorkshire.

6. There were six children in the Brontë family, two of whom died in infancy. Can you name them all?

7. Charlotte Brontë wrote four novels. A point for each one you can name.

8. On whom is Arthur Huntingdon in "The Tenant of Wildfell Hall" thought to be based?

9. Charlotte and Emily both spent time in Brussels. True or false?

10. Only one of the Brontë sisters married. Which one was it?

11. Which of Charlotte Brontë's novels is set at the time of the Napoleonic wars? Is it:

    a) "The Professor"   b) "Villette"   c) "Shirley" ?

12. Why was Branwell Brontë dismissed as tutor to the Robinson family?

13. All three sisters used pseudonyms when they wrote. A point for each one you know.

14. One of Charlotte Brontë's novels was published posthumously. Which one is it?

15. What are Angria and Gondal?

16. Who worked as a governess to the Ingham and the Robinson families?

17. "The Professor" was at first rejected for publication. True or false?

18. What are Cowan Bridge and Roe Head?

19. Branwell Brontë wrote plays and first introduced the idea of the 'Young Men's Magazine.' True or false?

20. Who fell in love with M. Heger while she was in Belgium?

21. Anne and Emily both died of the same disease. What was it?

22. In the preface to the second edition of "Jane Eyre" to whom does Charlotte Brontë dedicate the book?

23. Who is Arthur Bell Nichols?

24. Charlotte Brontë died only a few months after her wedding. What was the cause of her death?

25. Which one of her novels does Charlotte describe as "unromantic as Monday morning"?

# NAME THE BOOK OR THE PERSON

1. In which book would you find Mr Rochester?

2. Cathy and Heathcliff are characters in one of the novels. What is it called?

3. Of the seven novels written by the Brontë sisters, three are named after characters in them. Which ones are they?

4. Match these characters to the novels in which they are found:

   a) Helen Huntingdon    b) Shirley Keeldar
   c) Edgar Linton
   i) "Shirley"                ii) "Wuthering Heights"
   iii) "The Tenant of Wildfell Hall"

5. "My godmother lived in a handsome house in the clean and ancient town of Bretton."
   This is the opening line from one of Charlotte Brontë's novels but which one is it?

6. "there was a mystery at Thornfield;"
   Can you identify the book?

7. "All true histories contain instruction;" This is the opening line from "Agnes Grey".   True or false?

8. Only one of Charlotte Brontë's novels is narrated by a male character but which one is it?
   Extra points if you can name the character.

9. Who is the tenant of Wildfell Hall?

# NAME THE BOOK OR THE PERSON

10. The following characters are all housekeepers but do you know in which novels they are found?

   a) Mrs Dean   b) Mrs Barratt   c) Mrs Fairfax
   i) "Villette"   ii) "Jane Eyre"   iii) "Wuthering Heights"

11. "There was no possibility of taking a walk that day." Where does this opening line belong?

12. Caroline Helstone, Robert Moore and Mrs Pryor are all found in one of Charlotte Brontë's works but which one is it?
   Is it: a) "Shirley"   b) "The Professor"   c) "Jane Eyre" ?

13. Which of her sister's novels does Charlotte Brontë describe as having been "hewn in a wild workshop, with simple tools, out of homely materials."?

14. Who in a novel by Anne Brontë runs a school with her mother in a seaside town?

15. Ginevra Fanshawe, Dr John and Madame Beck are all found in the same novel but which one is it?

16. "You must go back with me to the autumn of 1827."
   This is an opening line but from which novel is it taken?
   Is it: a) "Jane Eyre"   b) "Wuthering Heights"
                c) "The Tenant of Wildfell Hall"?

17. Match these characters to the books in which they are found:

   a) Grace Poole and Leah   b) Joseph and Zillah
   c) Rachel
   i) "Wuthering Heights"            ii) "Jane Eyre"
   iii) "The Tenant of Wildfell Hall".

18. In "Wuthering Heights" who is the tenant of Thrushcross Grange?

# NAME THE BOOK OR THE PERSON

19. Who is Miss Keeldar's tenant in "Shirley"?

20. "My narrative is not exciting, and above all, not marvellous;"
    This is from "Villette". True or false?

21. Helen and Ellen are both narrators but where would you find them?

22. "The name of governess, I soon found, was a mere mockery as applied to me, my pupils had no more notion of obedience than a wild unbroken colt."
    This is from a novel by Anne Brontë but which one is it?

23. "'My dear,' said Mrs Pryor, 'you are very young to be a governess, and not sufficiently robust: the duties a governess undertakes are often severe.' "
    Is this from:   a) "Villette"   b) "Shirley"   c) "Jane Eyre" ?

24. "I shall never forget that first lesson, nor all the undercurrent of life and character it opened up to me."
    Can you name the novel?

25. "Reader, perhaps you were never in Belgium?"
    Where is this from?

26. Which novel has an opening chapter entitled "Levitical"?
    Is it:   a) "Villette"   b) "The Professor"   c) "Shirley" ?

27. "Warm, jealous and haughty, I knew not till now that my nature had such a mood; he gathered me near his heart. I was full of faults; he took them and me all home."
    Can you name the book and identify the characters?

28. Who has a dog called Pilot and in which book will you find a dog called Tartar?

29. "This was a strange house, where no corner was sacred from intrusion, where not a tear could be shed, nor a thought pondered, but a spy was at hand to note and divine."
    Is this from:       a) "Villette"       b) "The Professor"
                        c) "Agnes Grey"?

30. "This was a demoniac laugh - low, suppressed, and deep - uttered, as it seemed, at the very keyhole of my chamber door."  Can you name the book?

31. "I could not half tell what an infernal house we had." Where is this from and who is speaking?

32. Only one of the novels is not narrated in the first person. Which one is it?

33. In which novel by Charlotte Brontë would you find the characters Zoraïde Reuter and Yorke Hunsden?

34. "And now I think I have said sufficient." These are the final words of "Jane Eyre".       True or false?

35. Which novel ends with the word "Farewell."?

# MAIN CHARACTERS

1. What is Mr Rochester's first name?

2. " 'I should like to be a governess.'" Is this:
   a) Jane Eyre      b) Agnes Grey      c) Shirley Keeldar ?

3. "He is a dark-skinned gypsy in aspect, in dress and manners a gentleman:" Who is he?

4. Lucy Snowe is the heroine of "Villette". True or false?

5. Which heroine saves the hero from a fire in his room?

6. Heathcliff does not have a first name. True or false?

7. Who in a novel by Charlotte Brontë is born in Geneva with a Swiss father and an English mother?

8. "He came of a foreign ancestry by the mother's side," This is from "Shirley" but who is he?

9. Who is governess to the Murray children? Is it:
   a) Jane Eyre      b) Agnes Grey      c) Shirley Keeldar ?

10. Can you match the following names correctly? :
    a) Helen Huntingdon  b) Lucy Snowe   c) Jane Eyre
    i) Mr Rochester   ii) Gilbert Markham   iii) M. Paul

11. Which heroine in a novel by Anne Brontë paints pictures?

12. " 'You are patient, I am choleric; you are quiet and pale, and I am tanned and fiery; you are a strict Protestant, and I am a sort of lay Jesuit: but we are alike - there is affinity between us.' "
    Is this from:      a) "Villette"      b) "Agnes Grey"
    c) "The Professor" ?

13. " 'he's more myself than I am. Whatever our souls are made of, his and mine are the same;' "
    Who is speaking and about whom?

# MAIN CHARACTERS

14. Match the characters to the books in which they are found:
    a) William Crimsworth     b) Robert Moore
    c) Edward Weston
    i) "Agnes Grey"     ii) "Shirley"     iii) "The Professor"

15. " 'you are not pretty any more than I am handsome' " and
    " 'I am old enough to be your father,' "
    Can you identify the characters?

16. " 'Lucy, take my love. One day share my life. Be my dearest,
    first on earth.' "
    This is from "Villette" but who is speaking?

17. Who, whilst teaching in Belgium, falls in love with one of
    his pupils and marries her?

18. Name the books from which the following lines are taken:
    a) "' They gave me a man's name; I hold a man's position'
       " and "I have pistols and can use them."
    b) "Women are supposed to be very calm generally: but women
       feel just as men feel: they need exercise for their faculties,"

19. In which novel would you find the following lines?
    "And there I beheld a tall, lady-like figure, clad in black.
    Her face was towards me, and there was something in it,
    which, once seen, invited me to look again."

20. The following is the first meeting of the hero and heroine.
    Who are they?
    " 'Are you injured, sir?'
    I think he was swearing, but I am not certain; however, he
    was pronouncing some formula which prevented him from
    replying to me directly."

21. Can you match correctly the names and occupations of
    the following ?
    a) Farmer    b) Mill owner    c) Teacher
    i) M. Paul    ii) Gilbert Markham    iii) Robert Moore

22. "He made me love him without looking at me."
    This is from "Wuthering Heights". True or false?

23. "She never had power to conceal her passion, it always set her whole complexion in a blaze."
    Can you identify her?

24. Who can read and write French and German but is short sighted?

25. "He was naturally a little man, of unreasonable moods."
    Name the character.

26. "I felt it a misfortune that I was so little, so pale, and had features so irregular and so marked."
    Who is this?

27. " 'Be with me always-take any form-drive me mad! only *do* not leave me in this abyss where I cannot find you!' "
    Who is speaking?

28. " 'tree-shadows will take your shape; in the white sprays of hawthorn I shall imagine glimpses of you. Lina, you will haunt me.' "
    This is from "Shirley" but who is speaking?

29. " 'The human heart is like India-rubber; a little swells it, but great deal will not burst it.' "
    This is Edward Weston in "Agnes Grey". True or false?

30. "I turned from moon and stars, opened a side-door, and went in."
    Where is this from?

# WEDDINGS AND MARRIAGES

1. "Reader, I married him."   Where is this from?

2. "I was married in summer, on a glorious August morning."
   This is from a novel by Anne Brontë but who says it?

3. " 'I am not cherishing love-dreams: I am only thinking because
   I cannot sleep; of course he will marry Shirley.' "
   Can you identify the characters?

4. Who does Heathcliff marry?

5. "and there she stood by the window, clad all in white, and
   white of a most diaphanous texture;"
   This is from "The Professor" but can you identify the bride?

6. "The marriage cannot go on: I declare the existence of an
   impediment."   Where is this from?

7. All these characters in "The Tenant of Wildfell Hall" are
   married by the end of the novel. But who marries who?
   a) Frederick Lawrence        i) Mary Millward
   b) Richard Wilson            ii) Esther Hargrave
   c) Ralph Hattersley          iii) Millicent Hargrave

8. Who does Graham Bretton marry in "Villette"?
   Is it:  a) Ginevra   b) Polly   c) Lucy ?

9. " 'Marry! Will birds pair? Of course, it is her intention and
   resolution to marry when she finds a suitable match.' "
   This is from "The Professor" and refers to Zoraïde Reuter.
   True or false?

10. Who marries who? Match up the right names.
    a) Agnes Grey               i) Robert Moore
    b) Shirley Keeldar          ii) Louis Moore
    c) Caroline Helstone        iii) Edward Weston

11. " 'Bigamy is an ugly word! I meant, however, to be a bigamist;' " Who is he?

12. Mr. Sweeting marries Miss Dora Sykes in a novel by Charlotte Brontë but which one is it?

13. In "Wuthering Heights" who marries Edgar Linton?

14. " 'My bride is here," he said, again drawing me to him, 'because my equal is here, and my likeness.' "
Can you identify the characters?

15. Can you name the character who runs away from her husband but who later returns to nurse him?

16. There are two Mrs Rochesters in "Jane Eyre" and two Mrs Heathcliffs in "Wuthering Heights." How many of them can you name?

17. Who at the end of "Villette" elopes with Alfred de Hamal?

18. " 'I would be an excellent wife to him if he did marry me: I would tell him of his faults (for he has a few faults), but I would study his comfort, and cherish him, and do my best to make him happy.' " Is this:
a) Frances Henri   b) Caroline Helstone   c) Lucy Snowe?

19. In "Shirley" Robert Moore proposes to two women. Can you name them both?

20. "The first of June arrived at last and Rosalie Murray was transmuted into Lady Ashby. Most splendidly beautiful she looked in her bridal costume." Is this from:
a) "Agnes Grey"   b) "Shirley"   c) "Jane Eyre" ?

21. "sir, it removed my veil from its gaunt head, rent it in two parts, and flinging it on the floor, trampled on them." This is from "Wuthering Heights".   True or false?

22. " 'But I do think if I was you, Miss Helen, I'd look very well before I leaped. I do believe a young lady can't be too careful who she marries.' "
Can you identify the book? An extra point if you can name the character too.

23. In "Wuthering Heights" who is married at Gimmerton Chapel?

24. M. Pelet and Zoraïde Reuter are married in "The Professor". True or false?

25. The following two extracts are both from "Jane Eyre" but can you identify the characters?
a) " 'Nonsense, again! Marry! I don't want to marry, and never shall marry.' "
b) " 'A missionary's wife you must-shall be. You shall be mine:' "

26. "it is not enough to say that I no longer love my husband - I HATE him! The word stares me in the face like a guilty confession but it is true:" From which book are these lines taken? Can you also name the characters?

# FAMILIES

1. In which novel would you find the Earnshaws?

2. Mrs Reed is Jane Eyre's aunt. True or false?

3. In "The Tenant of Wildfell Hall" who is Helen's brother?

4. Match these families to the novels in which they are found:
   a) Blanche and Mary Ingram  b) the Linton family
   c) the Wilson family.
   i) "The Tenant of Wildfell Hall"  ii) "Jane Eyre"
   iii) "Wuthering Heights".

5. William Crimsworth in "The Professor" has a brother. Is he called:  a) Edward     b) Charles     c) Yorke ?

6. " 'Mother, you are better to me than ten wives yet.' "
   This is Graham Bretton in "Villette". True or false?

7. "Of six children, my sister Mary and myself were the only two that survived the perils of infancy and early childhood." This is from a novel by Anne Brontë but which one is it?

8. In "Shirley" who is Caroline Helstone's mother?

9. Of the seven novels, in which five do the main characters have children?

10. All the following are found in "Wuthering Heights" but can you match the children to their parents?
    a) Hareton Earnshaw          i) Isabella and Heathcliff
    b) Linton                    ii) Cathy and Edgar
    c) Catherine Linton          iii) Hindley and Frances

11. "(I had long ceased to regard Mr. Crimsworth as my brother...)"   This is from "Villette".   True or false?

12. " 'Hereafter she is only my sister in name: not because I disown her but because she has disowned me.' "
    This is from "Wuthering Heights" but can you identify the brother and sister?

13. " 'I never had a sister - you never had a sister; but it flashes on me at this moment how sisters feel towards each other.' "
    Name the book and the characters.

14. In which novel do two sisters both marry clergymen? Is it
    a) "Villette" b) "Agnes Grey" c) "Shirley" ?

15. Match these families to the books in which they are found:
    a) The Yorke family b) Madame and Mademoiselle Reuter
    c) Madame Beck and her children
    i) "The Professor" ii) "Shirley" iii) "Villette".

16. What is the relationship between Jane Eyre and the Rivers family?

17. " 'his mother's heart dances at the sight of him.' " This is from a novel by Charlotte Brontë but which one is it?

18. In "The Tenant of Wildfell Hall" Mr Wilmot and Annabella Wilmot are cousins. True or false?

19. " 'for a worse man, a harder master, a more brutal brother than you are has seldom existed.' "
    Is this from: a) "Jane Eyre" b) "The Professor"
    c) "Wuthering Heights"?

20. " 'I will not have it said that my niece is a governess.' "
    This is from "Shirley" but can you identify the characters?

# FAMILIES

21. Agnes Grey and Edward Weston have three children. A point for each one you can name.

22. In "Wuthering Heights" both Linton and Hareton have a cousin. Who is she?

23. Ginevra and Polly ("Villette") are related but in what way?

24. Who in "Shirley" has a sister called Hortense and a brother called Louis?

25. "My mother, being at once highly accomplished, well informed, and fond of employment, took the whole charge of our education on herself, with the exception of Latin-which my father undertook to teach us-so that we never even went to school."
This is from "Agnes Grey". True or false?

26. Who, in a novel by Charlotte Brontë, has a son called Victor?

27. "But unluckily the Varens, six months before, had given me this fillette Adèle, who she affirmed, was my daughter; and perhaps she may be though I see no proofs of such grim paternity written in her countenance:"
Can you identify the book and the character?

28. " 'the person you call your cousin Robert is sometimes a dreamer, who lives elsewhere than in Cloth-hall and counting house.' "
Is this from:  a) "Shirley"   b) "Villette"   c) "Jane Eyre"?

# HOUSES, LOCATIONS AND SETTINGS

1. In which novel would you find Thrushcross Grange?

2. Lowood School, Gateshead Hall and Millcote are all found in the same novel but which one is it?

3. Two of Charlotte Brontë's novels are set abroad. A point for each one you can name.

4. Which two novels have the names of houses in their titles?

5. "Happily the architect had foresight to build it strong: the narrow windows are deeply set in the wall, and the corners defended with large, jutting stones."
   Name the book from which these lines are taken.

6. "It was three stories high, of proportions not vast, though considerable; a gentleman's manor-house, not a nobleman's seat: battlements round the top gave it a picturesque look."
   Can you identify the house and the book?

7. Grassdale Manor and Staningley are both found in the same novel.
   Is it:   a) "The Tenant of Wildfell Hall"   b) "Agnes Grey"
   c) "Shirley" ?

8. In which novel would you find Wellwood and Horton Lodge?

9. "This was neither a grand nor a comfortable house: within as without it was antique, rambling and incommodious."
   These lines are from "Shirley" but can you identify the house?

# HOUSES, LOCATIONS AND SETTINGS.

10. Which novel is named after a city?

11. Crimsworth Hall and the Rue Notre Dame aux Neiges are both found in "The Professor". True or false?

12. " 'Do you not find it a desolate place to live in?' "
    This is from "Wuthering Heights". True or false?

13. The following are from novels by Charlotte, Emily and Anne Brontë. But who has written what? Extra points if you can identify the books.
    a) "On the hilltop above me sat the rising moon; pale yet as a cloud but brightening momently; she looked over Hay, which, half lost in trees, sent up a blue smoke from its few chimneys;"
    b) "I was out on the hill with the reapers. A light wind swept over the corn; and all nature laughed in the sunshine. The lark was rejoicing among the silvery floating clouds."
    c) "My landlord hallooed for me to stop, ere I reached the bottom of the garden, and offered to accompany me across the moor. It was well he did, for the whole hill-back was one billowy white ocean;"

14. In which novel would you find the parishes of Whinbury, Briarfield and Nunnely?
    Is it: a) "Shirley"  b) "Agnes Grey"  c) "Jane Eyre" ?

15. "I saw what a fine street was the Rue Royale, and, walking leisurely along its broad pavement, I continued to survey its stately hotels,"
    Is this from "Villette" or "The Professor" ?

16. "I looked with timorous joy towards a stately house; I saw a blackened ruin." Name the book.

# HOUSES, LOCATIONS AND SETTINGS

17. Which novel has chapters entitled: "The Parsonage", "The Park" and "The Sands" ?

18. "a superannuated mansion of the Elizabethan era, built of dark grey stone - venerable and picturesque to look at, but doubtless cold and gloomy enough to inhabit, with its thick stone mullions and little latticed panes,"
Where would you find this description and name the "mansion" if you can.

19. "Hollow's Cottage" and "Briarmains" are the titles of chapters in "Wuthering Heights". True or false?

20. "Opening an inner door, M. Paul disclosed a parlour or salon - very tiny, but I thought it very pretty. Its delicate walls were tinged like a blush; its floor was waxed; a square of brilliant carpet covered its centre."
Can you name the book from where these lines are taken?

21. "The mill yawned all ruinous with unglazed frames; the yard was thickly bestrewn with stones and brickbats,"
Is this from: a) "Shirley" b) "Jane Eyre" c) "The Professor"?

# JANE EYRE

1. At the beginning of "Jane Eyre" who is Jane living with?

2. "The red-room was a spare chamber, very seldom slept in:"
   Who is locked in this room?

3. The following three people are all connected with Lowood
   School but can you identify them correctly?
   a) Mr Brocklehurst     i) the superintendent
   b) Helen Burns         ii) the director
   c) Maria Temple        iii) Jane's friend and fellow pupil

4. How does Jane find a position at Thornfield?

5. "A snug, small room; a round table by a cheerful fire; an
   arm-chair high-backed and old fashioned, wherein sat the
   neatest imaginable little elderly lady, in widow's cap, black
   silk gown, and snowy muslin apron;"
   Who is she?

6. At Thornfield, what is the name of Jane's pupil?
   Is it:  a) Adèle     b) Leah     c) Céline ?

7. " 'you cannot always be sure whether he is in jest or earnest,
   whether he is pleased or the contrary: you don't thoroughly
   understand him in short-at least, I don't:' "
   Can you identify the two characters?

8. Who is Grace Poole?

9. "it *was* an incident of no moment, no romance, no interest
   in a sense; yet it marked with change one single hour of a
   monotonous life."
   What is the incident?

10. The following are all descriptions of Jane but who says what?
    a) " 'You are a strange child, Miss Jane,' "
    b) " 'She looks sensible but not at all handsome.' "
    c) " 'No wonder you have rather the look of another world' "
    i) Mr Rochester     ii) St John Rivers     iii) Bessie.

11. "A wealthy Englishman's passion for a French dancer," Can you identify the two characters?

12. Jane believes Mr Rochester is going to marry one of the Ingram girls. Is she called Blanche or Mary?

13. Who dresses up as a gypsy woman telling fortunes?

14. " 'olive complexion, dark and clear: noble features; eyes rather like Mr Rochester's, large and black, and as brilliant as her jewels.' "
    This is a description of Blanche Ingram. True or false?

15. Who is Bertha Antonietta Mason?

16. On her death bed, Mrs Reed gives Jane something to read. What is it?

17. Who wanted to adopt Jane?

18. The following are Jane Eyre and Mr Rochester describing themselves but who says what:
    a) " 'I am passionate but not vindictive' "
    b) " 'I once had a kind of rude tenderness of heart' "

19. Two sisters and their brother live at Moor House. A point for each one you can name.

20. Who is Hannah?

21. Jane is describing two men but can you identify them?
    a) "I told her he was rather an ugly man, but quite a gentleman;"
    b) " 'He is a good and a great man; but he forgets, pitilessly, the feelings and claims of little people, in pursuing his own large views;"

22. " 'And your will shall decide your destiny,' he said. 'I offer you my heart, my hand, and a share of all my possessions.' "
    Name the two characters.

23. Bertha Mason has a brother but what is his name?
    Is it: a) John    b) Henry    c) Richard ?

24. Someone stops the wedding between Jane and Mr Rochester but who is it?

25. " 'It was a discoloured face - it was a savage face. I wish I could forget the roll of the red eyes and the fearful blackened inflation of the lineaments!' "   Who is this ?

26. Mary Rivers sets up a village school for girls and offers Jane the job of school mistress.   True or false?

27. " 'One does not jump, and spring, and shout hurrah! at hearing one has got a fortune; one begins to consider responsibilities and ponder business;' "
    This is Jane speaking but who has left her a fortune?

28. Can you identify the two characters in the following extracts?
    a) " 'I want you to give up German and learn Hindustani.' "
    b) " 'I say again, I will be your curate, if you like, but never your wife.' "

29. Who sets fire to Thornfield and dies when she jumps from the roof?

30. "he left England: he went to India."
    Who is he?

31. Do you know who is living at Ferndean "blind, and a cripple"?

32. "he eventually recovered the sight of that one eye" and "When his first-born was put into his arms, he could see that the boy had inherited his own eyes, as they once were - large, brilliant, and black."
    Who is he?

# WUTHERING HEIGHTS

1. Who is the opening narrator of "Wuthering Heights"?

2. Name the person who tells him "Heathcliff's history".

3. In what year does the novel begin?
   Is it:   a) 1807      b) 1778     c) 1801 ?

4. Mr Lockwood meets two servants at Wuthering Heights? Can you name them both?

5. What names does he find scratched into the "ledge of a window"?

6. Who is this?: "an elderly, nay, an old man: very old, perhaps, though hale and sinewy. "The Lord help us!" he soliloquised in an undertone of peevish displeasure, while relieving me of my horse:"

7. Catherine and Isabella both have brothers. What are their names?

8. Who finds Heathcliff in the streets of Liverpool?

9. Why do the Earnshaws give him the name of Heathcliff?

10. Hindley is sent away to college but after his father's death returns. Who does he bring with him?

11. Heathcliff is bitten by a bulldog belonging to the Lintons. True or false?

12. The following are all said of Cathy but who says what?
    a) "but she was so proud, it became really impossible to pity her distresses,"
    b) " 'she is so immeasurably superior to them - to everyone on earth - is she not, Nelly?' "
    c) " 'You've made me afraid and ashamed of you',"

13. Who throws a "tureen of hot apple sauce" over Edgar Linton and is then locked in the garret?

14. What is Mrs Dean's first name?

15. "he possessed the power to depart, as much as a cat possesses the power to leave a mouse half killed, or a bird half eaten." Who is he?

16. Who "had never been heard of since the evening of the thunder-storm;" and does not return for three years?

17. "He had room in his heart only for two idols - his wife and himself; he doted on both, and adored one,"
    Who is he?

18. The following are said by Mrs Dean, Isabella and Cathy but who says what?
    a) " 'he's a fierce, pitiless, wolfish man.' "
    b) " 'He's a lying fiend! a monster, and not a human being!' "
    c) " 'Rough as a saw-edge, and hard as winstone! The less you meddle with him the better.' "

19. What is the name of Heathcliff and Isabella's son and who does he marry?

20. " 'I've dreamt in my life dreams that have stayed with me ever after, and changed my ideas: they've gone through and through me like wine through water, and altered the colour of my mind.' "
    Who is speaking?

21. In the following extract, Catherine is one of three characters. Can you name the other two?:
    "An instant they held asunder, and then how they met I

hardly saw, but Catherine made a spring, and he caught her, and they were locked in an embrace from which I thought my mistress would never be released alive;"

22. Who dies two hours after giving birth to a daughter?

23. Name the character who "had mortgaged every yard of land he owned, for cash to supply his mania for gaming;" and who is "the mortgagee"?

24. "His honest, warm, and intelligent nature shook off rapidly the clouds of ignorance and degradation in which it had been bred."
Who does this describe? Is it:   a) Linton   b) Hareton ?

25. At the close of the novel, who is going to marry on New Year's Day?

26. Who does Mrs Dean find dead in the panelled bed at Wuthering Heights?

# THE TENANT OF WILDFELL HALL

1. What is the name Helen Huntingdon assumes whilst living at Wildfell Hall?

2. Helen has a son called Arthur. True or false?

3. The narrator of the book is male but what is his name? Is it:  a) Fergus Markham   b) Frederick Lawrence   c) Gilbert Markham ?

4. "she was the vicar's younger daughter, and a very engaging little creature, for whom I felt no small degree of partiality;" Who is she?

5. " 'No one can be happy in eternal solitude.' " Who says this? Is it:  a) Helen   b) Eliza   c) Gilbert ?

6. Mr Lawrence is "the young squire whose family had formerly occupied Wildfell Hall". How is he related to Helen?

7. "Her hair was raven black, and disposed in long, glossy ringlets....the forehead was lofty and intellectual, the nose a perfect aquiline, and the features in general unexceptionable"  Who is she?

8. When Gilbert first visits Helen, what is she doing?

9. "Had I killed him? an icy hand seemed to grasp my heart and check its pulsation, as I bent over him, gazing with breathless intensity upon the ghastly upturned face." Can you name both characters?

10. Millicent Hargrave is Annabella Wilmot's niece. True or false?

11. Who is "too great a flirt to be married, according to her own assertion,"? Is it:  a) Annabella  b) Millicent?

12. Who are Mr Grimsby, Mr Hattersley and Mr Hargrave?

13. " 'I did not know the strength and depth of your attachment"
    This is Helen speaking to Gilbert. True or false?

14. Who is Rachel?

15. "I wished I had not married him."
    Who says this and who is she speaking about?

16. Are the following true or false?
    a) Helen's diary forms a large part of the novel.
    b) Gilbert tells the story in the form of a letter to a friend.

17. Whose aunt is Mrs Maxwell?

18. " 'Well my dear, ask your uncle what sort of company he keeps, and if he is not banded with a set of loose, profligate young men whom he calls his friends' "
    This is Peggy Maxwell but who is she talking about?

19. Lord Lowborough marries Millicent Hargrave. True or false?

20. In the following extract, can you identify all four characters:
    "I would not suspect my husband falsely on this man's accusation, and I would not trust him unworthily - I must know the truth at once. I flew to the shrubbery. Scarcely had I reached it, when a sound of voices arrested my breathless speed."

21. Why does Helen return to Arthur?

22. "As for myself, I need not tell you how happily my Helen and I have lived together, and how blessed we are in each other's society,"
    This is Gilbert but can you name the person he is writing to?

# SHIRLEY

1. Three curates are introduced in the first chapter of "Shirley". A point for each one you can name.

2. "he is what you would probably call, at first view, rather a strange-looking man: for he is thin, dark, sallow; very foreign of aspect, with shadowy hair carelessly streaking his forehead:"
   Who is he?

3. Mr Helstone is the rector of Briarfield. True or false?

4. Who lives at Briarfield Rectory with her uncle?

5. Can you identify the character from the following lines:
   "She did not choose to adopt English fashions because she was obliged to live in England; she adhered to her old Belgian modes, quite satisfied that there was a merit in so doing."

6. " 'my mill is my castle.' "
   Do you know who says this?

7. Who "had never known her mother as she was taken from her in infancy, and had not since seen her."?

8. One chapter is entitled "Old Maids". How many old maids are there? A point for each one you can name.

9. "He made no pretence of comprehending women,"
   Is this: a) Mr Helstone b) Robert Moore c) Mr Yorke ?

10. Who "in a distant sense" is the cousin of Robert, Hortense and Louis?

11. " 'Your heart is a lyre, Robert; but the lot of your life has not been a minstrel to sweep it, and it is often silent.' "
    This is Caroline Helstone speaking. True or false?

12. " 'We're thrown out o' work wi' these frames: we can get naught to do; we can earn nought. What is to be done?' "
William Farren is speaking but who is he talking to?

13. The Yorke family live at Briarmains. True or false?

14. Who is "the heiress of Fieldhead" and who is her ex-governess ?

15. "They parted in the garden without kiss, scarcely without pressure of hands:"
Who are they?

16. Whose mill is attacked by rioters?

17. The following extracts refer to the same two characters. Can you name them both?
    a) "she was, compared with the heiress, as a graceful pencil-sketch compared with a vivid painting."
    b) "The minds of the two girls being toned in harmony, often chimed very sweetly together."

18. "To avoid excitement" was one of whose "aims in life"?

19. Who does Caroline believe Robert will marry?

20. Can you identify the two characters from the following:
    a) "Indolent, wilful, picturesque, and singularly pretty was her aspect."
    b) " 'No one who looks at my slow face can guess the vortex sometimes whirling in my heart,' " ?

21. "She followed the steps of the night, on its pathway of stars....she was with Moore in spirit the whole time: she was at his side: she heard his voice: she gave her hand into his hand: it rested warm in his fingers."
    Who is she?

22. Who falls dangerously ill and is nursed by Mrs Pryor?

23. The following is an exchange between mother and daughter. Can you name them both?
    " 'just now I feel as if I could almost grow to your heart.' "
    " 'Daughter! we have been long parted: I return now to cherish you again.' "

24. Who is shot by Michael Hartley?
    Is it:      a) Mr Yorke    b) Robert Moore    c) Mr Helstone ?

25. "To be so near him - though he was silent - though he did not touch so much as her scarf fringe, or the white hem of her dress, affected her like a spell."
    This is Robert and Caroline. True or false?

26. "This morning there were two marriages solemnized in Briarfield Church."
    Whose marriages are they?

# VILLETTE

1. At the beginning of "Villette" where is Lucy living and with whom?

2. Mrs Bretton has a son. What is his name?

3. "Relieved of her wrapping, she appeared exceedingly tiny; but was a neat, completely fashioned little figure, light, slight and straight."
Who is she?

4. Who does Polly live with?

5. "My mistress being dead, and I once more alone, I had to look out for a new place."
Who is Lucy's mistress?    Is it:    a) Miss Marchmont b) Mrs Leigh  c) Mrs Barratt ?

6. Lucy goes first to London but can you name the "continental port" she then sails to?

7. Who does she meet on board ship?
Is it: a) Polly  b) Graham Bretton  c) Ginevra Fanshawe ?

8. "She paced the deck once or twice backwards and forwards; she looked with a little sour air of disdain at the flaunting silks and velvets,"
Who is she?

9. How does Lucy learn of Madame Beck's school and where is it?

10. "No ghost stood beside me, nor anything of spectral aspect; merely a motherly, dumpy little woman, in a large shawl, a wrapping-gown, and a clean, trim nightcap."
This is Madame Beck. True or false?

11. "He entered: a small, dark, and spare man, in spectacles." Who is he?

12. What is M. Paul's full name?

13. " 'Lucy, I wonder if anyone will comprehend you altogether' " Who says this? Is it:
a) Madame Beck    b) Ginevra    c) Polly/Paulina?

14. Who turns out the pocket of Lucy's dress and goes through all her things?

15. "his profile was clear, fine and expressive...his chin was full, cleft, Grecian, and perfect."
Who is he?

16. Name the character who collapses with a "nervous fever" outside a church?

17. " 'You know, monsieur, I only see you in classe - stern, dogmatic, hasty, imperious.' "
Lucy is speaking but who is she talking to?

18. Dr John and Graham Bretton are the same person. True or false?

19. "I remember him heroic" and "Really that little man was dreadful"
Lucy is speaking of two men but who are they?

20. What sort of apparition does Lucy see?

21. Who is Mlle de Bassompierre?

22. When Lucy and Graham are at the theatre, fire breaks out. Who is hurt in the crush?

23. "his mind was indeed my library, and whenever it was opened to me, I entered bliss."
Who is he?

24. Who establishes Lucy as "directrice" of her own school?

25. "He watched me still; he gently raised his hand to stroke my hair; it touched my lips in passing; I pressed it close, I paid it tribute:"
Can you name the two characters?

26. M. Paul goes to the West Indies for three years. True or false?

# THE PROFESSOR

1. "I have therefore consented to its publication."
   The book is "The Professor" but who has given consent?

2. "I declined both the Church and matrimony".
   Who says this?

3. Lord Tynedale and the Hon. John Seacombe are both related to William but in what way?
   Are they:   a) cousins     b) uncles     c) brothers-in-law ?

4. "In face, I resembled him though I was not so handsome; my features were less regular; I had a darker eye and a broader brow - in form I was greatly inferior - thinner, slighter, not so tall."
   Can you name the two characters?

5. Name the person who employs William as "second clerk to manage the foreign correspondence of the house."?

6. Who is Yorke Hunsden?

7. *"you'll never be a tradesman  "* This is Yorke Hunsden talking to William. True or false?

8. William is given a letter of introduction to Mr Brown in Belgium but do you know who gives it to him?

9. At whose school is William first employed?

10. The following is a description of Frances Henri. True or false?
    " she could not, I thought, be more than six or seven and twenty; she was as fair as a fair Englishwoman; she had no cap; her hair was nut-brown and she wore it in curls;"

11. William is offered teaching work at another school. Whose is it?

12. " 'Surely she's not going to make love to me,' said I. 'I've heard of old Frenchwomen doing odd things in that line; and the goûter? They generally begin such affairs with eating and drinking I believe.' " Who is she?

13. Eulalie, Hortense, Caroline and Adèle are all William's pupils. True or false?

14. "She had precisely the same shape of skull as Pope Alexander the Sixth;" Who is she?

15. Can you identify the two characters from the following extract:
" 'for deny it as you will, I am certain you have cast encouraging glances on that schoolboy Crimsworth; he has presumed to fall in love, which he dared not have done unless you had given him room to hope.' "

16. "She was dressed, like all the rest, in a dark stuff gown and a white collar; her features were dissimilar to any there, not so rounded, more defined, yet scarcely regular."
Is this a description of Frances Henri or Madame Pelet?

17. What does Frances Henri teach?

18. "the marriage was solemnized at St. Jacques;"
Whose marriage is it?

19. Why does Mr Vandenhuten help William find a new job?

20. " 'Master, I consent to pass my life with you.' "
Who is she?

21. Who wants to continue teaching after she is married?

22. "The Professor" ends with the words: " 'Papa, come!' "
True or false?

# AGNES GREY

1. What is the name of Agnes's father and what is his profession?

2. Agnes is a governess in two families. Can you name them both?

3. "I could not help feeling that she was cold, grave, and forbidding"
   This is a description of Mrs Bloomfield. True or false?

4. How does Agnes find a position with the Murray family?

5. There are four children in the Murray family. A point for each one you can name.

6. Who is "a strapping hoyden of about fourteen" and who is "a handsome, dashing lady of forty, who certainly required neither rouge nor padding to add to her charms,"?

7. Mary Grey, Agnes's sister, marries a vicar called Mr Richardson. True or false?

8. Can you name the rector of Horton?

9. "She was tall, and slender, yet not thin; perfectly formed, exquisitely fair, but not without a brilliant, healthy bloom;"
   Who is she?

10. Who is the new curate?

11. Name the person who says: "Who is to form a young lady's tastes, I wonder, if the governess doesn't do it?"

12. "besides, I must have *somebody* to flirt with;"
    Who says this?

13. The following is a description of Edward Weston. True or false?
    "In stature, he was a little, a very little, above the middle size; perfectly symmetrical in figure, deep-chested, and strongly built; the outline of his face would be pronounced too square for beauty, but to me it announced decision of character;"

14. Who says: "reformed rakes make the best husbands,"?
    Is it:   a) Rosalie Murray    b) Nancy Brown
    c) Mrs Murray ?

15. Harry Meltham, Mr Green, Mr Hatfield and Sir Thomas Ashby are all "admirers" of Rosalie but which one does she marry?

16. Who is "a widow, whose son was at work all day in the fields, and who was afflicted with an inflammation of the eyes,"?

17. Where does Agnes first meet Mr Weston?

18. "But I intend him to feel my power."
    Rosalie is speaking here but who is she talking about?

19. Who is Agnes describing in the following lines:
    "I could discover no beauty in those marked features, that pale hollow cheek, and ordinary dark brown hair; there might be intellect in the forehead, there might be expression in the dark grey eyes: but what of that?"

20. "Two days after, a letter from Mary told me his life was despaired of, and his end seemed fast approaching."
    Who is he?

21. Agnes is invited to stay at Ashby Park but who invites her?

22. Agnes and Edward Weston meet up again on the beach. True or false?

# ANSWERS: THE BRONTË SISTERS AND THEIR FAMILY

1. Charlotte, Emily and Anne.

2. Charlotte Brontë and Emily Brontë.

3. Haworth, Yorkshire.

4. "The Tenant of Wildfell Hall" and "Agnes Grey".

5. a) True.      b) False. Cornwall.

6. Maria, Elizabeth (both of whom died in infancy), Charlotte, Emily, Anne and Branwell.

7. "The Professor", "Jane Eyre", "Villette" and "Shirley".

8. Branwell Brontë.

9. True.

10. Charlotte.

11. c) "Shirley".

12. He had an affair with Mrs Robinson.

13. Currer, Ellis and Acton Bell.

14. "The Professor".

15. Fantasy worlds invented by the Brontë children.

16. Anne Brontë.

17. True.

18. Schools attended by the Brontë sisters.

19. True.

20. Charlotte.

21. Tubercolosis.

22. William Thackeray.

23. Charlotte's husband.

24. Complications in her pregnancy.

25. "Shirley".

# ANSWERS: NAME THE BOOK OR PERSON

1. " Jane Eyre".

2. "Wuthering Heights".

3. "Jane Eyre", "Shirley" and "Agnes Grey" .

4. Helen Huntingdon    - "The Tenant of Wildfell Hall"

   Shirley Keeldar    - "Shirley"

   Edgar Linton    - "Wuthering Heights"

5. "Villette".

6. "Jane Eyre".

7. True.

8. "The Professor". William Crimsworth.

9. Helen Huntingdon (using the name of Mrs Graham).

10. Mrs Dean    - "Wuthering Heights"

    Mrs Barratt    - "Villette"

    Mrs Fairfax    - "Jane Eyre"

11. "Jane Eyre".

12. a) "Shirley".

13. "Wuthering Heights".

14. Agnes Grey.

15. "Villette".

16. c) "The Tenant of Wildfell Hall"

17. Grace Poole and Leah    - "Jane Eyre"

    Joseph and Zillah    - "Wuthering Heights"

    Rachel    - "The Tenant of Wildfell Hall"

18. Mr. Lockwood.

19. Robert Moore.

20. False. "The Professor".

21. Helen in "The Tenant of Wildfell Hall" and Ellen in "Wuthering Heights".

22. "Agnes Grey".

23. b) "Shirley".

24. "Villette".

25. "The Professor".

26. c) "Shirley".

27. "Villette". Lucy Snowe and M. Paul.

28. Mr Rochester. Tartar is in "Shirley".

29. a) "Villette".

30. "Jane Eyre".

31. "Wuthering Heights". Mrs Dean.

32. " Shirley" .

33. "The Professor".

34. False. "Agnes Grey".

35. "Villette" .

# ANSWERS: MAIN CHARACTERS

1. Edward.

2. b) Agnes Grey

3. Heathcliff.

4. True.

5. Jane Eyre.

6. True.

7. Frances Henri.

8. Robert Moore.

9. b) Agnes Grey.

10. Helen Huntingdon and Gilbert Markham. Lucy Snowe and M. Paul. Jane Eyre and Mr Rochester.

11. "The Tenant of Wildfell Hall".

12. a) "Villette".

13. Cathy Earnshaw about Heathcliff.

14. William Crimsworth: "The Professor"

    Robert Moore: "Shirley"

    Edward Weston: "Agnes Grey"

15. Jane Eyre and Mr Rochester.

16. M. Paul.

17. William Crimsworth

18. a) "Shirley Keeldar" b) "Jane Eyre"

19. "The Tenant of Wildfell Hall".

20. Jane Eyre and Mr Rochester.

21. Farmer      - Gilbert Markham.

    Mill owner   - Robert Moore.

    Teacher      - M. Paul.

22. False. "Jane Eyre".

23. Cathy Earnshaw.

24. William Crimsworth.

25. M. Paul.

26. Jane Eyre.

27. Heathcliff.

28. Robert Moore.

29. True.

30. "Jane Eyre".

1. "Jane Eyre".

2. Gilbert Markham ( "The Tenant of Wildfell Hall" ) .

3. Caroline Helstone and Robert Moore.

4. Isabella Linton.

5. Frances Henri.

6. "Jane Eyre".

7. Frederick Lawrence and Esther Hargrave;

   Richard Wilson and Mary Millward;

   Ralph Hattersley and Millicent Hargrave.

8. b) Polly.

9. True.

10. Agnes Grey marries Edward Weston.

    Shirley Keeldar marries Louis Moore.

    Caroline Helstone marries Robert Moore.

11. Mr Rochester.

12. "Shirley".

13. Catherine Earnshaw

14. Mr Rochester and Jane Eyre.

15. Helen Huntingdon.

16. Bertha Mason and Jane Eyre.

    Isabella Linton and Catherine Linton.

17. Ginevra Fanshawe.

18. b) Caroline Helstone.

19. Shirley and Caroline.

20. a ) "Agnes Grey" .

21. False. "Jane Eyre".

22. "The Tenant of Wildfell Hall".  Rachel.

23. Cathy and Edgar.

24. True.

25. a) Jane Eyre   b) St. John Rivers.

26. "The Tenant of Wildfell Hall".

    Helen and Arthur Huntingdon.

# ANSWERS: FAMILIES

1. "Wuthering Heights".

2. True.

3. Frederick Lawrence.

4. Blanche and Mary Ingram: "Jane Eyre".

   The Linton family: "Wuthering Heights".

   The Wilson family: "The Tenant of Wildfell Hall".

5. a) Edward .

6. True.

7. "Agnes Grey".

8. Mrs Pryor.

9. Cathy ("Wuthering Heights");     Jane Eyre;

   Agnes Grey;    Frances Henri ("The Professor");

   Helen Huntingdon ("The Tenant of Wildfell Hall") .

10. Hareton Earnshaw - Hindley and Frances;

    Linton - Isabella and Heathcliff;

    Catherine Linton - Cathy and Edgar.

11. False. "The Professor".

12. Edgar and Isabella Linton.

13. "Shirley".   Caroline and Shirley.

14. b) "Agnes Grey".

15. The Yorke family - "Shirley"

    Madame and Mademoiselle Reuter - "The Professor"

    Madame Beck and her children - "Villette".

16. They are cousins.

17. "Villette".

18. False. They are uncle and niece.

# ANSWERS: FAMILIES

19. b) "The Professor".

20. Mr Helstone and Caroline.

21. Edward, Agnes and Mary.

22. Catherine Linton.

23. They are cousins.

24. Robert Moore.

25. True.

26. Frances Henri ("The Professor").

27. "Jane Eyre".   Mr Rochester.

28. a) "Shirley".

# ANSWERS: HOUSES, LOCATIONS AND SETTINGS

1. "Wuthering Heights".

2. "Jane Eyre".

3. "Villette" and "The Professor".

4. "Wuthering Heights" and "The Tenant of Wildfell Hall".

5. "Wuthering Heights".

6. Thornfield Hall, "Jane Eyre".

7. a) "The Tenant of Wildfell Hall".

8. "Agnes Grey".

9. Fieldhead.

10. "Villette".

11. True.

12. False. "The Tenant of Wildfell Hall".

13. a) Charlotte Brontë - "Jane Eyre"

    b) Anne Brontë - "The Tenant of Wildfell Hall"

    c) Emily Brontë - "Wuthering Heights".

14. a) "Shirley".

15. "The Professor".

16. "Jane Eyre".

17. "Agnes Grey".

18. "The Tenant of Wildfell Hall". Wildfell Hall

19. False. "Shirley".

20. "Villette".

21. a) "Shirley".

# ANSWERS: JANE EYRE

1. The Reed family.

2. Jane Eyre.

3. Mr Brocklehurst     - the director

   Helen Burns        - friend and fellow pupil

   Maria Temple      - the superintendent

4. She advertises in the newspaper.

5. Mrs Fairfax.

6. a) Adèle

7. Mrs Fairfax speaking of Mr Rochester.

8. The woman who looks after Bertha Mason.

9. Jane's first meeting with Mr Rochester.

10. a) Bessie b) St John Rivers c) Mr Rochester.

11. Mr Rochester and Céline Varens.

12. Blanche

13. Mr Rochester.

14. True.

15. Mr Rochester's wife.

16. A letter from her uncle

17. John Eyre.

18. a) Jane Eyre    b) Mr Rochester

19. Diana, Mary and St John Rivers.

20. She is the Rivers' servant.

21. a) Mr Rochester    b) St John Rivers.

22. Mr Rochester and Jane Eyre.

23. c) Richard.

24. Mr. Briggs, a solicitor.

25. Bertha Mason.

26. False. St John.

27. Her uncle, John Eyre.

28. a) St John Rivers   b) Jane Eyre

29. Bertha Mason.

30. St John Rivers.

31. Mr Rochester.

32. Mr Rochester.

# ANSWERS: WUTHERING HEIGHTS

1. Mr Lockwood.
2. Mrs Dean.
3. 1801.
4. Joseph and Zillah.
5. Catherine Earnshaw, Catherine Heathcliff, Catherine Linton.
6. Joseph.
7. Hindley and Edgar.
8. Mr Earnshaw.
9. It was the name of their son who had died in childhood.
10. His wife, Frances.
11. False. Cathy.
12. a) Mrs Dean    b) Heathcliff    c) Edgar Linton.
13. Heathcliff.
14. Ellen/Nelly.
15. Edgar Linton.
16. Heathcliff.
17. Hindley Earnshaw.
18. a) Cathy    b) Isabella    c) Mrs Dean
19. Linton.  He marries Catherine Linton.
20. Cathy.
21. Heathcliff and Mrs Dean.
22. Cathy.
23. Hindley.  Heathcliff.
24. b) Hareton.
25. Catherine Linton and Hareton Earnshaw.
26. Heathcliff.

# ANSWERS: THE TENANT OF WILDFELL HALL

1. Mrs Graham.
2. True.
3. c) Gilbert Markham
4. Eliza Millward.
5. a) Helen.
6. He is her brother.
7. Helen Huntingdon.
8. Painting.
9. Gilbert and Frederick Lawrence.
10. False. They are cousins.
11. a) Annabella.
12. Friends of Arthur Huntingdon.
13. True.
14. Helen's servant.
15. Helen. Arthur Huntingdon.
16. a) True. b) True.
17. Helen's.
18. Arthur Huntingdon.
19. False. Annabella Wilmot.
20. Mr Hargrave, Helen, Arthur and Annabella (Lady Lowborough)
21. To nurse Arthur who is unwell.
22. Halford.

1. Mr. Donne, Mr. Malone and Mr Sweeting.

2. Robert Moore.

3. True.

4. Caroline Helstone.

5. Hortense Moore.

6. Robert Moore.

7. Caroline Helstone.

8. Two. Miss Mann and Miss Ainly.

9. a) Mr Helstone.

10. Caroline.

11. True.

12. Robert Moore.

13. True.

14. Shirley Keeldar. Mrs Pryor.

15. Caroline and Robert.

16. Robert Moore's.

17. Caroline and Shirley.

18. Miss Mann's.

19. Shirley.

20. a) Shirley   b) Louis Moore.

21. Caroline.

22. Caroline.

23. Caroline and Mrs Pryor.

24. b) Robert Moore.

25. True.

26. Caroline and Robert.  Shirley and Louis.

# ANSWERS: VILLETTE

1. In Bretton with her godmother.

2. John Graham Bretton.

3. Paulina (Polly) Home.

4. Mrs Bretton.

5. a) Miss Marchmont.

6. Boue-Marine.

7. c) Ginevra Fanshawe.

8. Ginevra.

9. Through Ginevra who is a pupil there. Villette.

10. True.

11. M. Paul.

12. Paul David Carl (Carlos) Emanuel.

13. Polly (Paulina).

14. Madame Beck.

15. Dr John.

16. Lucy.

17. M. Paul.

18. True.

19. Dr John and M. Paul.

20. The ghost of a nun.

21. Paulina Home (Polly)

22. Paulina.

23. M. Paul.

24. M. Paul.

25. Lucy and M. Paul.

26. True.

# ANSWERS: THE PROFESSOR

1. Arthur Bell, Charlotte's husband.

2. William Crimsworth.

3. b) uncles.

4. William and Edward.

5. His brother, Edward.

6. A manufacturer and a mill owner.

7. True.

8. Yorke Hunsden.

9. M. Pelet.

10. False. Zoraïde Reuter.

11. Zoraïde Reuter's.

12. Madame Pelet.

13. True.

14. Juanna Trista.

15. M. Pelet talking to Zoraïde Reuter.

16. Frances Henri.

17. Lace-mending.

18. M. Pelet and Zoraïde Reuter.

19. Because William saved his son from drowning.

20. Frances Henri.

21. Frances Henri.

22. True.

# ANSWERS: AGNES GREY

1. Richard Grey. Clergyman.
2. The Bloomfields and the Murrays.
3. True.
4. She advertises in the paper.
5. John, Charles, Matilda and Rosalie.
6. Matilda and Mrs Murray
7. True.
8. Mr Hatfield.
9. Rosalie Murray.
10. Edward Weston.
11. Mrs Murray.
12. Rosalie.
13. True.
14. a) Rosalie
15. Sir Thomas Ashby.
16. Nancy Brown.
17. At Nancy Brown's cottage.
18. Edward Weston.
19. Herself.
20. Richard Grey, Agnes's father.
21. Rosalie.
22. True.